Shine bright in KS2 Science with CGP!

This fantastic CGP book is a great way to help pupils strengthen their understanding of Year 6 Science.

It's packed with short bursts of practice at the perfect level for Year 6 pupils. There's a fun puzzle for every section, and we've even included pre-topic tests so you can check pupils' prior knowledge before they get stuck in.

We've included full answers to every question, and a handy progress chart to make marking a breeze!

What CGP is all about

Our sole aim here at CGP is to produce the highest quality books — carefully written, immaculately presented and dangerously close to being funny.

Then we work our socks off to get them out to you — at the cheapest possible prices.

Contents

Section 1 – Living Things and Their Habitats

Section 2 – Animals Including Humans

Section 3 – Evolution and Inheritance

Section 4 – Light

Section 5 – Electricity

Section 6 – Mixed Practice

Published by CGP

Editors: Katie Fernandez, Rachel Hickman, Luke Molloy, Sarah Pattison, Charlotte Sheridan

Contributor: Paddy Gannon

With thanks to Katherine Faudemer and Kate Whitelock for the proofreading.

With thanks to Emily Smith for the copyright research.

ISBN: 978 1 78908 906 6

Clipart from Corel®

Illustrations by: Sandy Gardner Artist, email sandy@sandygardner.co.uk

Printed by Elanders Ltd, Newcastle upon Tyne.

Based on the classic CGP style created by Richard Parsons.

Getting Started

1. Fill in the gaps in the sentences below using words from the box.

insects	features	backbone	invertebrates	shell

Animals can be divided into two groups, called

vertebrates and .... Animals in the

same group share similar ....

Vertebrates are all animals with a ....

2. Use the classification key to find the names of the four organisms below.

A

B

C

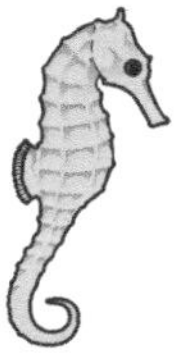

D

1)	Does it have wings?	YES NO	go to question 2. go to question 3.
2)	Does it have a beak?	YES NO	— it's a Mallard. — it's a Red Admiral.
3)	Does it have four legs?	YES NO	— it's a Mustang. — it's a Seahorse.

A .... C ....

B .... D ....

Test 1 — Classifying Organisms

Warm up

1. Sort the different living things into the correct columns in the table.

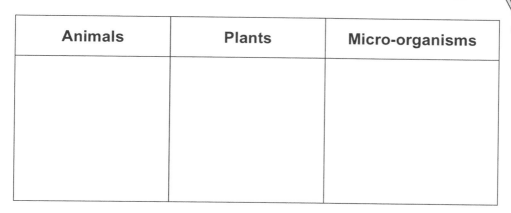

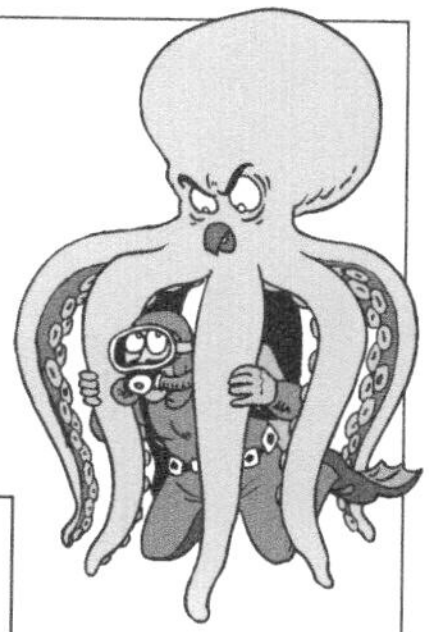

moss   bacteria

octopus   fox   oak tree

Animals	Plants	Micro-organisms

3 marks

2. a) What is meant by 'classification'?

....

....

1 mark

b) Why is classification important?
Tick the box next to the correct reason.

It helps to protect habitats. ☐

It can be used to identify living things. ☐

It shows how living things have changed over time. ☐

1 mark

3. Circle the type of vertebrate that best matches each sentence below.

This type of vertebrate doesn't lay eggs.

amphibian **mammal** **fish** **reptile**

This type of vertebrate doesn't breathe with lungs.

fish **reptile** **bird** **mammal**

2 marks

4. Dolphin babies are born live and breathe using lungs. What type of vertebrate are dolphins?

....

1 mark

5. Plants are a group of living things.

a) Give one feature that all plants have in common.

....

....

1 mark

b) Give one feature that some plants have that other plants don't.

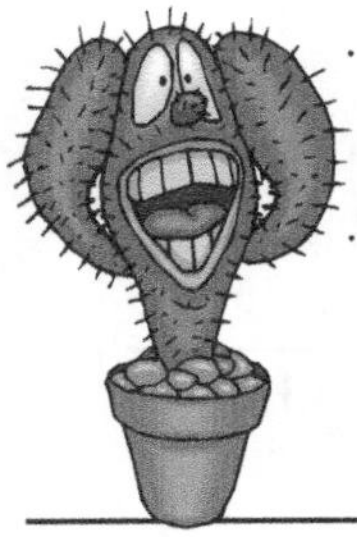

....

....

1 mark

6. Tick the correct box to show whether each statement is true or false.

	True	False
All bacteria are micro-organisms.	☐	☐
Moss is a type of micro-organism.	☐	☐
Micro-organisms can be really big.	☐	☐

3 marks

7. Look at this picture of an organism.

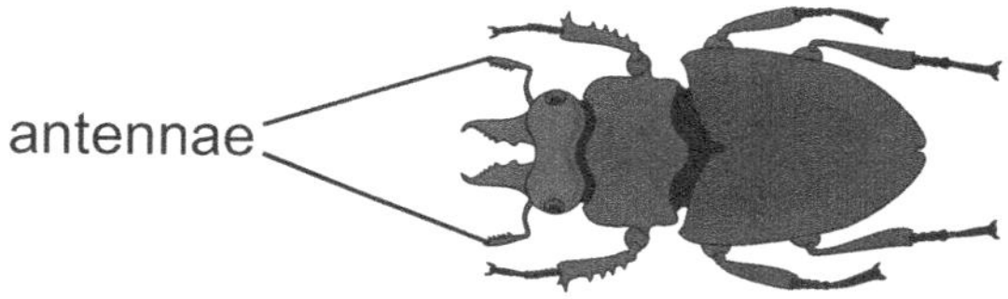

a) Fill in the information below. The first part has been done for you.

Does it have a backbone? ....No..........

Number of legs: ....

Number of body parts: ....

1 mark

b) Circle whether the organism is a vertebrate or an invertebrate, and write the name of the group that it belongs in.

This organism is **a vertebrate** / **an invertebrate**

and it belongs in the .... group.

2 marks

Score: / 16

Classification Wordsearch

There are lots of words you need to know when classifying organisms.
Can you find all of these words in the wordsearch?

ANIMALS	SNAILS	REPTILES	VERTEBRATES
PLANTS	BACKBONE	FISH	INVERTEBRATES
BIRDS	AMPHIBIANS	INSECTS	FLOWERING
WORMS	MAMMALS	SPIDERS	MICROORGANISMS

M	N	P	O	R	E	Q	S	W	T	Y	G	F	A	S
S	E	T	A	R	B	E	T	R	E	V	N	I	D	J
M	A	S	B	E	R	S	N	I	O	E	I	S	G	L
S	C	M	D	N	M	E	A	T	F	R	R	H	E	R
I	P	H	E	R	B	R	L	O	H	T	E	B	O	U
N	E	F	O	S	I	S	P	M	E	E	W	A	C	X
A	D	W	H	N	U	B	A	C	K	B	O	N	E	S
G	T	L	N	A	C	L	Y	K	D	R	L	I	T	E
R	M	R	F	I	L	S	U	T	P	A	F	M	R	A
O	L	Y	D	B	I	N	S	E	C	T	S	A	V	Y
O	K	V	E	I	E	A	N	P	O	E	R	L	S	A
R	F	A	R	H	Y	E	A	J	I	S	T	S	L	R
C	L	R	E	P	T	I	L	E	S	D	L	T	I	L
I	U	O	I	M	E	M	P	N	G	O	E	F	A	E
M	A	M	M	A	L	S	D	E	R	F	X	R	N	A
E	W	P	A	L	F	X	E	T	H	P	O	I	S	Z

Getting Started

1. Circle all the examples of exercise below.

driving **dancing** **playing football**

walking **sleeping** **eating fruit**

2. Here are some pictures of food.

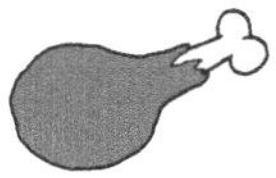
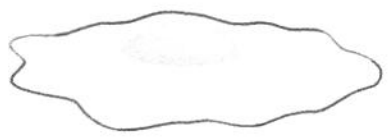

a) Circle the food group that all of these foods belong to.

carbohydrates **proteins** **fruit and vegetables**

b) Which of the foods below also belongs to this food group?
Tick one box.

☐ pasta ☐ water

☐ beans ☐ olive oil

3. Which part of the skeleton protects the heart?

....

Test 1 — The Circulatory System

10

Warm up

1. Use some of the words below to label the diagram.

heart **rib cage** **blood vessel**

lungs **bone**

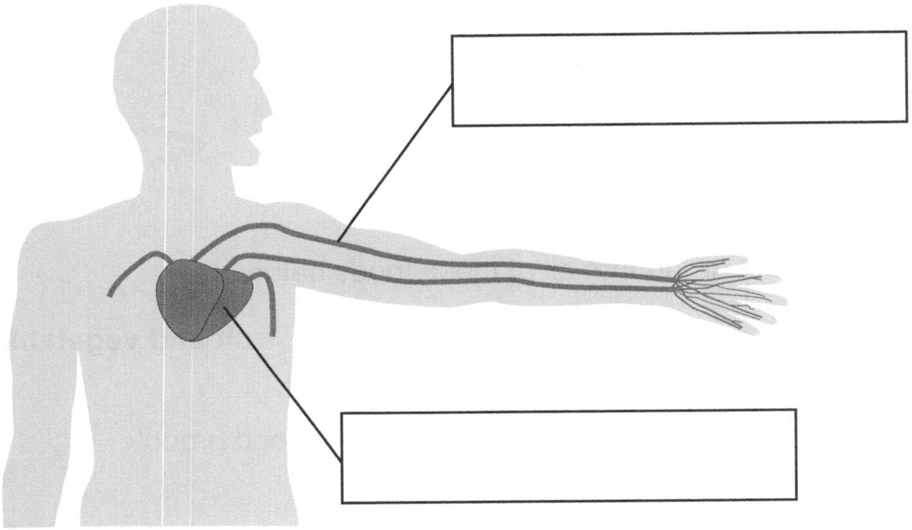

2 marks

2. What happens to the blood in the heart when the heart beats?

....

....

1 mark

3. Each sentence below describes a different type of blood vessel. Write the name of the blood vessel each sentence is describing.

This blood vessel carries blood away from the heart to the rest of body. ....

This blood vessel allows substances to move in and out of the blood. ....

This blood vessel carries blood from the rest of the body back to the heart. ....

3 marks

4. Look at the diagram of the heart below.
Complete the table to show which blood vessel is being labelled by each letter.

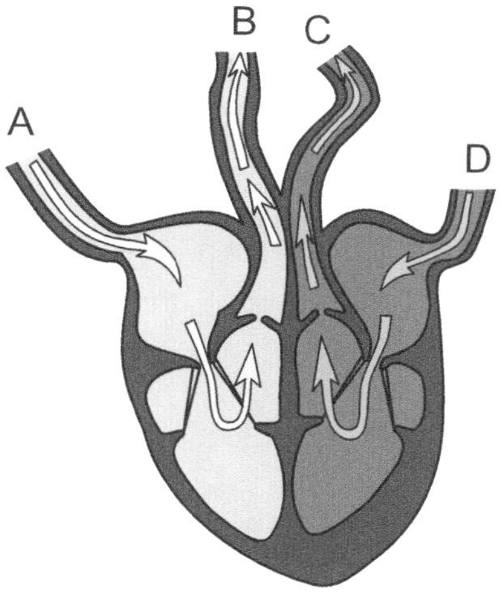

Blood Vessel	Letter
Vein from the lungs	
Artery to the body	
Vein from the body	
Artery to the lungs	B

2 marks

5. The circulatory system keeps blood circulating around the body.

a) Which of these things are moved around the body in the blood? Tick three boxes.

☐ carbon dioxide	☐ water	☐ bones
☐ capillaries	☐ kidneys	☐ nutrients

3 marks

b) We breathe gases in and out of our lungs.
Explain what happens to these gases when blood from the heart reaches the lungs.

....

....

....

2 marks

c) Draw arrows on the artery and vein below to show the direction that the blood flows in each vessel.

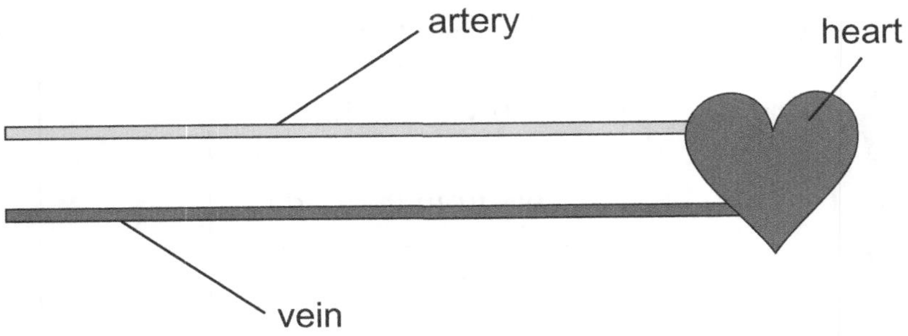

1 mark

Score: / 14

Test 2 – Keeping Healthy

Warm up

1. Draw lines to match each food with the food group it is in.

Food

butter 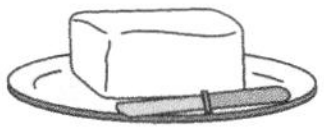

carrots 

bread 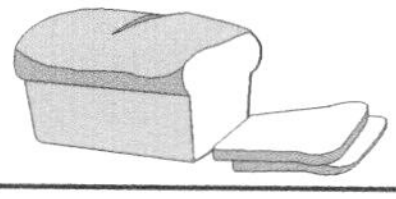

Food Group

Fats

Carbohydrates

Fruit and vegetables

2 marks

2. The organs in the diagram on the right remove water from the body. What is the name of organ A?

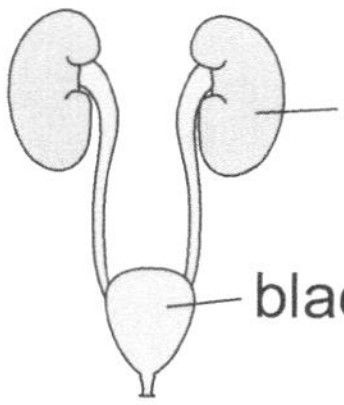

....

1 mark

3. Write down the name of a food that helps you grow.

....

1 mark

4. Tick two reasons why exercise is important.

It develops the kidneys. ☐

It helps you sleep. ☐

It helps towards a balanced diet. ☐

It strengthens the heart. ☐

2 marks

5. Smoking and drinking alcohol are both health risks.

a) Write down one way smoking can damage the body.

....

1 mark

b) Write down one way drinking alcohol can damage the body.

....

1 mark

c) What is the name of the chemical in cigarettes that makes smoking addictive?

....

1 mark

6. Use some of the words in the list below to fill in the gaps in the sentences. You can only use each word once.

large **stomach** **small** **water**

sugar **oxygen** **digestive** **blood** **liver**

Nutrients from food are absorbed into the ....

from the .... intestine.

.... is absorbed into the body in the

.... intestine.

4 marks

7. Give two ways you can maintain a healthy lifestyle.

....

....

2 marks

8. Why do we need fibre in our diet?

....

....

1 mark

Score: / 16

Crack the Code

Use the key below to decipher the coded words relating to this section.
The first one has been started for you.

A	B	C	D	E	F	G	H	I	J	K	L	M
J	E	T	N	R	Y	Q	O	D	S	P	L	V

N	O	P	Q	R	S	T	U	V	W	X	Y	Z
K	C	W	I	F	M	G	Z	X	B	A	H	U

MBQD ⟶ V [E] _ _

YBXEC ⟶ _ _ [ ] _ _

IEZTJ ⟶ _ [ ] _ _ _

BVBEOQJB ⟶ _ _ _ [ ] _ _ _ _

DZCEQBDCJ ⟶ _ _ _ _ _ _ _ [ ] _

OQEOZLXCHEF JFJCBS ⟶ _ _ _ _ _ _ _ _ _ _ _ [ ] _ _ _ _ _ _

Unscramble the letters in the boxes to reveal an extra word below:

[ ] [ ] [ ] [ ] [ ] [ ]

Section 3 – Evolution and Inheritance

Getting Started

1. Fill in the sentences about the environment.
Use the words in the box. You will not need to use all of the words.

damaged	**organisms**	**decorated**
habitat	**friends**	**food**

The environment that a living thing lives in is called

its .... If this environment is

.... , the .... living there

may die if they no longer have the conditions they need,

e.g. .... and shelter.

2. The four steps below should describe how a fossil is made,
but two of the statements are slightly incorrect.
Put a tick next to the two statements that are correct,
and a cross next to the two statements that are incorrect.

Dead animals and plants mix with mud and sand at the surface of lakes and seas. ☐

The mud and sand stick together to form layers of rock, trapping the dead animals and plants. ☐

The hard bits of the animals and plants rot away quickly. ☐

The shapes of the plants and animals are left behind in the rock. ☐

Test 1 – Inheritance and Adaptations

Warm up

1. Tick the correct box to show whether each statement is true or false.

	True	False
All offspring from the same parents will have the same characteristics.	☐	☐
Only some of an offspring's characteristics are inherited from their parents.	☐	☐
Offspring from the same parents can look identical to each other.	☐	☐

3 marks

2. Look at the adaptations labelled on the plant.

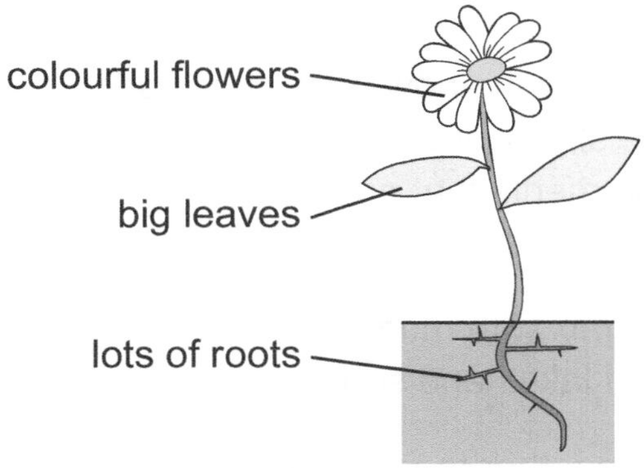

Pick one adaptation and describe how it helps the plant to survive.

....

....

....

1 mark

3. Shown below are pictures of a mother and a father dog.

Their offspring has the two characteristics below. Write which of the parents each characteristic is most likely to have come from.

Patterned fur ....

Long tail ....

2 marks

4. Look at the picture of a fennec fox.

Having big ears helps the fox to keep cool.

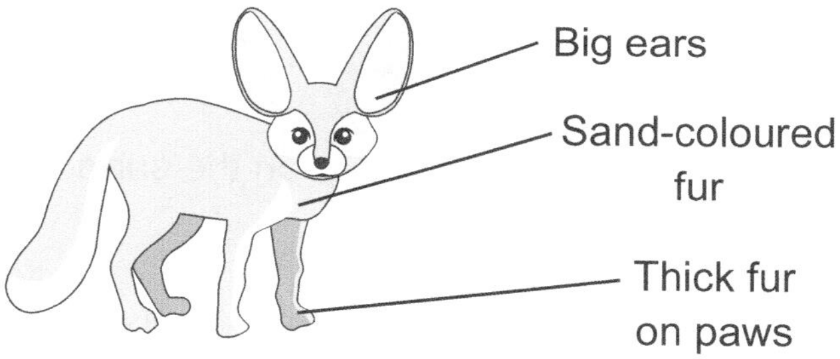

a) Tick the box next to the type of habitat this fox is most likely to live in.

A damp rainforest ☐ A hot desert ☐

A snowy mountain ☐ A murky pond ☐

1 mark

b) Give one other reason why having big ears is a useful adaptation.

....

....

1 mark

5. Match each adaptation of a polar bear to the reason why it is useful.

White appearance	To help move around on the snow.
Two layers of fur and a layer of fat	To keep warm.
Large paws	To be less likely to be seen in the snow.

2 marks

6. Plants in the rainforest grow very close together.
Different plants in the rainforest have different adaptations.

a) Tick two adaptations that would help a tree in the rainforest get enough light.

A very smooth trunk ☐ A very tall trunk ☐

Leaves with pointy tips ☐ Large leaves ☐

2 marks

Some smaller plants grow high up on the surface of the trunks of big trees.

b) Which of the adaptations above would be useful for a big tree to have, to stop smaller plants growing on it?

....

1 mark

c) Explain why these smaller plants would need to be adapted differently to other plants in order to get nutrients and water.

....

....

1 mark

Score: / 14

Test 2 – Evolution

10

Warm up

1. Fill in the gaps in the sentences below using the words **more** or **less**.

In the wild, some elephants do not develop tusks.

Elephants are sometimes hunted for their tusks.

Elephants without tusks are .... likely to be hunted, so are .... likely to survive. This means they are .... likely to have offspring than elephants with tusks. This means that there will likely be .... elephants without tusks than elephants with tusks over time.

4 marks

2. Draw a line to match each fossil to the animal it is most similar to.

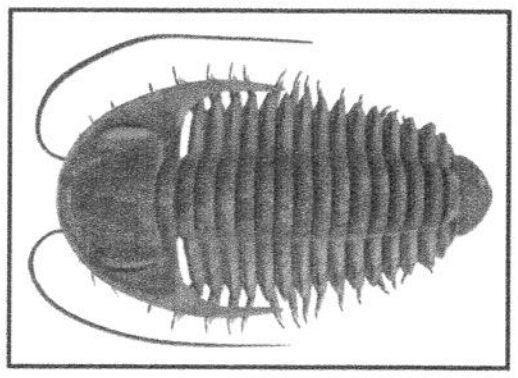

2 marks

3. Scientists have found fossils that look similar to living things today.

a) Why don't fossils look exactly the same as the living things that exist today?

....

.... 1 mark

b) Scientists haven't found fossils similar to all of the living things that exist today. Circle two reasons why this might be.

Not all living things become fossils.	All of the fossils have been found.
Fossils take one hundred years to make.	Not all of the fossils that exist have been found.

2 marks

4. Circle the correct words in the following paragraph about the evolution of giraffes.

Long ago, a group of animals ate leaves from trees.
When there were no more leaves on the **lower / upper** parts of the trees, some of the animals found it hard to reach the food.
The animals with slightly **longer / shorter** necks could reach the leaves higher up. These animals were **more / less** likely to survive and produce **offspring / parents**, who inherited the **longer / shorter** necks.

3 marks

5. An aye-aye is a type of lemur. To get food, an aye-aye uses its middle finger to pull grubs out of little holes in trees. Aye-ayes with shorter middle fingers cannot get grubs as easily as aye-ayes with longer middle fingers.

a) Put a tick in the box next to the type of aye-aye that is most likely to survive.

An aye-aye with a short, wide middle finger. ☐

An aye-aye with a short, narrow middle finger. ☐

An aye-aye with a long, wide middle finger. ☐

An aye-aye with a long, narrow middle finger. ☐

1 mark

Aye-ayes use their long, bushy tails to help them balance while climbing trees. A longer tail is better for balancing than a short tail.

b) Explain why aye-ayes born with short tails are less likely to pass on this characteristic than aye-ayes born with long tails.

....

....

....

....

....

3 marks

Score: / 16

Evolutionary Crossword

Complete the crossword containing the key words for this section, then use the letters in the grey boxes to complete the surname of a famous scientist who helped to develop the idea of Clue 5.

Across

2 The shape of a dead animal or plant, found in a rock.

4 A feature of a plant or animal, which helps it to survive in its habitat.

5 How living things change over time.

6 The children of a living thing.

Down

1 Where an animal or plant lives.

3 Differences in living things.

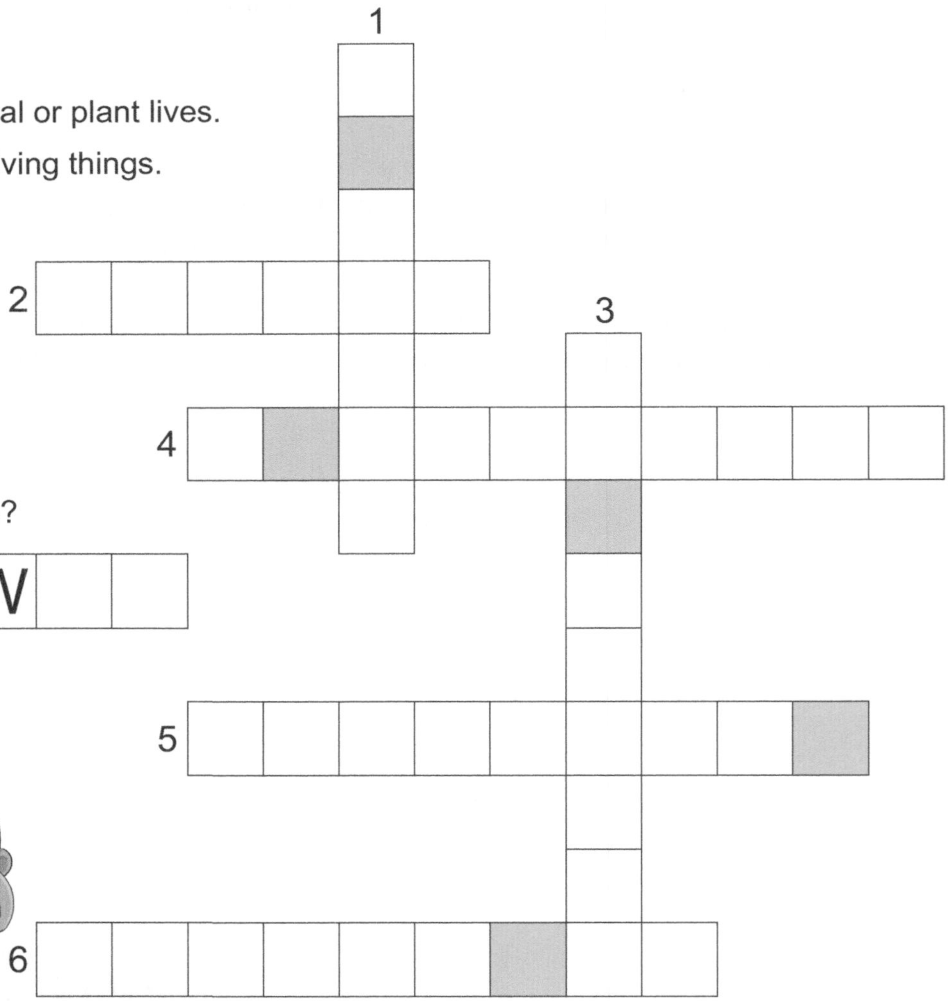

What is the surname?

			W		

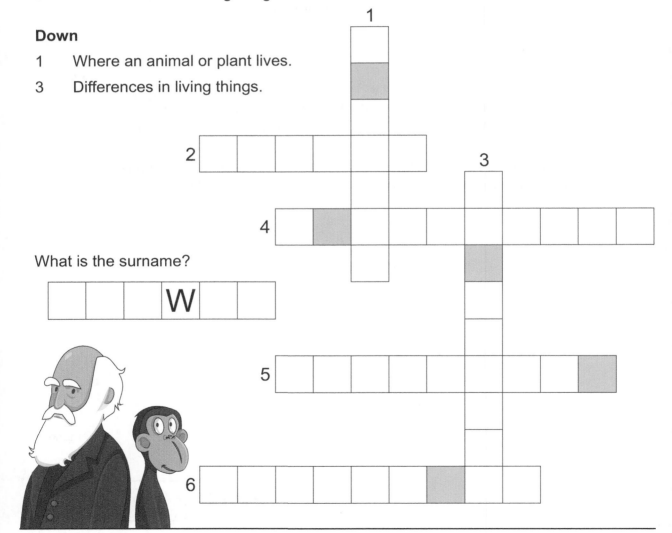

Getting Started

1. Circle all of the objects below that give out light.

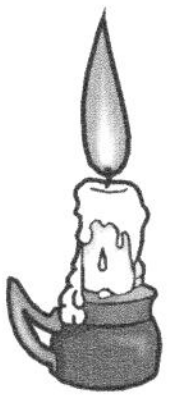

2. Complete the sentences by putting a circle around the correct word in each set of brackets.

If something (**opaque** / **transparent**) is in the way of a light source,

it produces a shadow.

The closer the light source (**the larger** / **the curvier**) the shadow is.

3. What happens to light when it hits a mirror?

....

Test 1 — Light, Shadows and Reflection

Warm up

1. Look at the sentences about light below and tick whether they are true or false.

	TRUE	FALSE
We see things when light enters our eyes.	☐	☐
We can only see objects that give out light.	☐	☐

2 marks

2. Cross out the wrong option in this sentence.

An object's shadow is **the same shape as the light source / the same shape as the object**.

1 mark

3. A student has drawn this picture to show light rays hitting a mirror.

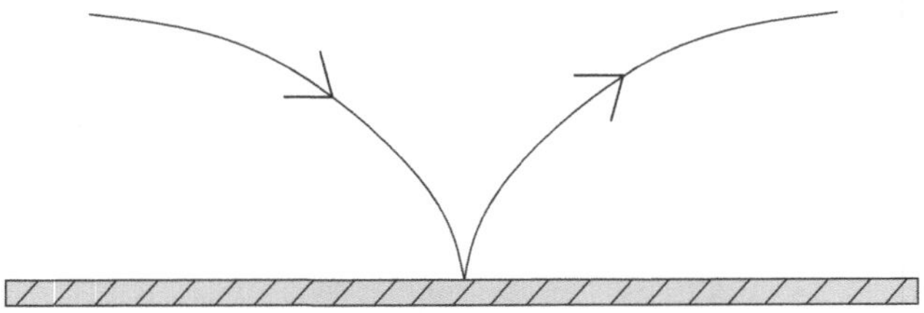

What is wrong with the light rays in the picture? Explain your answer.

....

....

....

2 marks

4. Tick the picture below that shows the correct shadow of the cheese.

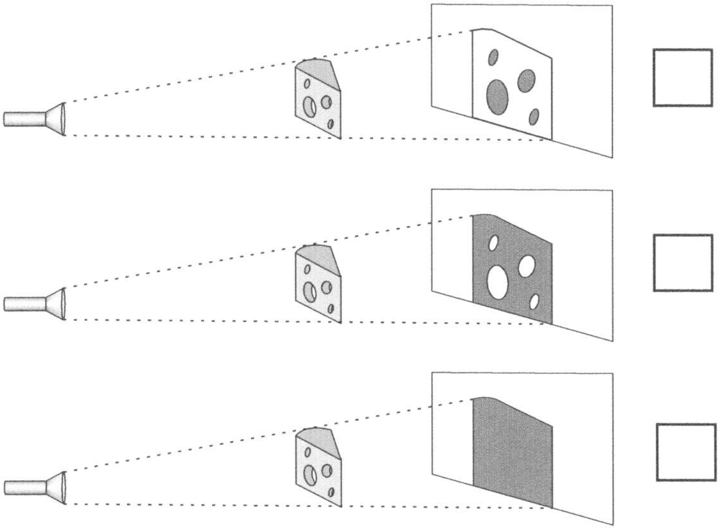

1 mark

5. A woman can see her car in this picture.

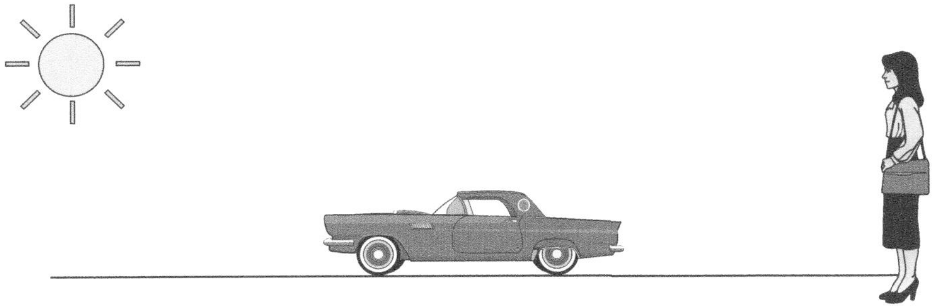

a) On the picture, draw an arrow to show a light ray hitting the car.

1 mark

b) Use some of the words from the box to complete the sentences.

road	**absorbs**	**woman**
twists	**Sun**	**reflects**

Light travels from the .... to the car.

Light .... off the car and into her eyes.

2 marks

6. A boy lives in a house next to a road.
The picture shows this from above.

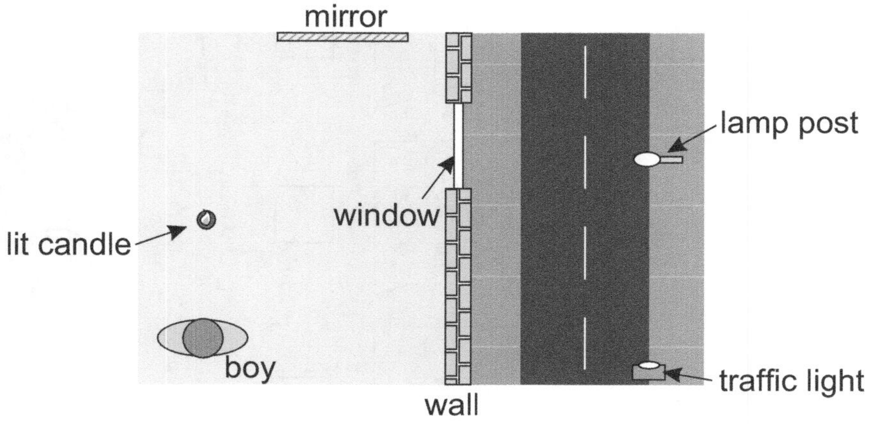

a) The boy can see the candle in his house. Explain why.

....

....

2 marks

The mirror and window allow the boy to see an object outside from where he is standing.

b) Which object will it be?

....

1 mark

c) Explain how the boy can see this object.

....

....

....

2 marks

Score: / 14

Path Plotter

Use the clues at the bottom of the page to fill in the missing words in the path.
Then use each of these words **once** to complete the sentence.

Path →

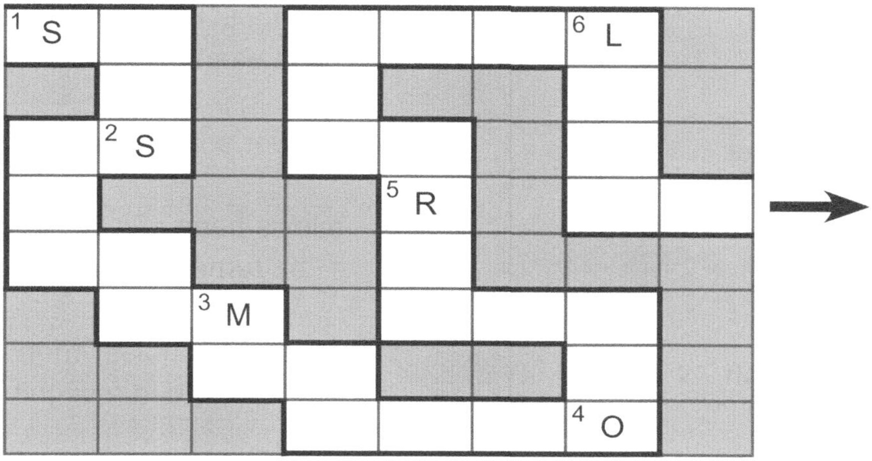

Complete the sentence:

.... from the .... hits a .... ,

causing it to .... onto an .... object and make

a .... behind the object.

Clues

1.

2.

3.

4. An .... object can block the Sun's light.

5. Light can .... off an object and into your eyes.

6. .... travels in straight lines.

Getting Started

1. Draw lines to connect each part of a circuit with its function.

cell	connects components so that electricity can flow
buzzer	a power source for a circuit
wire	allows parts of a circuit to be turned on and off
switch	makes a noise when connected in a circuit

2. Circle the items below that need electricity to work.

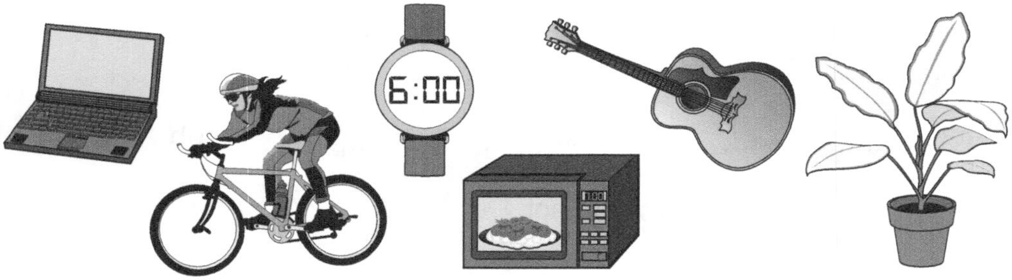

3. For each circuit below, put a tick in the box if the bulb will light.
Put a cross if it won't light.

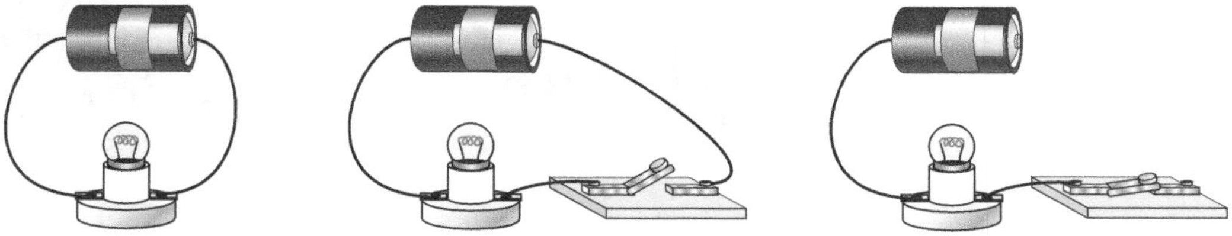

☐ ☐ ☐

Test 1 — Circuit Components and Symbols

Warm up

1. Label the circuit symbols below.

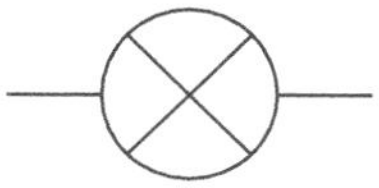

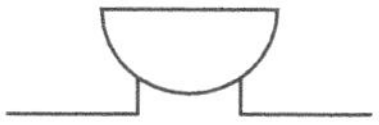

3 marks

2. Circle the buzzer that will make the quietest sound.

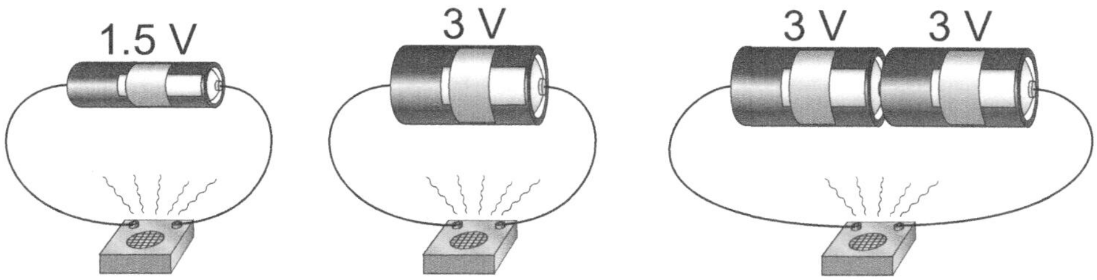

1 mark

3. Use some of the words below to complete the sentences.

cells **motors** **circuit** **bulbs** **voltage** **switch**

You can increase the brightness of a bulb in a circuit

by adding more .... You could also

use cells with a higher ....

2 marks

4. Look at this picture of a circuit.
Draw a circuit diagram of the circuit in the box below.

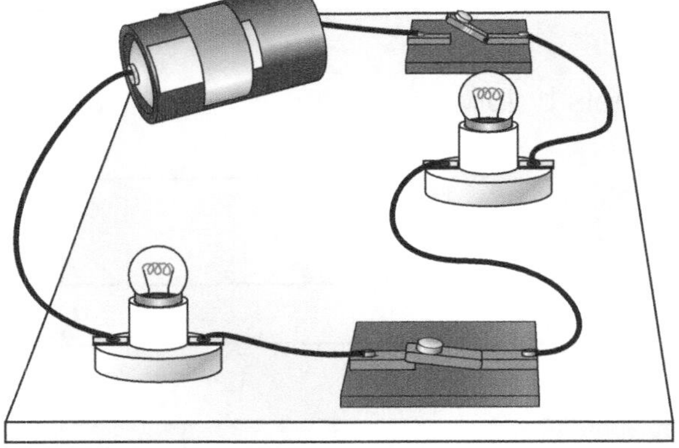

4 marks

5. There are two reasons why the bulb in the circuit on the right won't light.
Circle the two reasons.

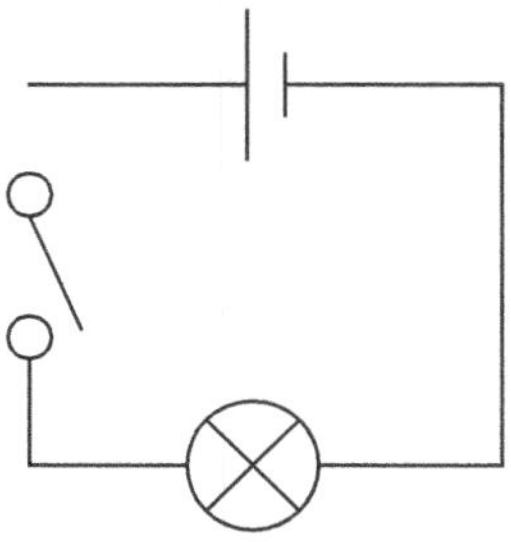

the switch is closed	**there is only one cell**
the switch is open	**a wire is missing**

2 marks

6. Omar is building a circuit to make an electronic quiz box. When the contestant knows the answer, they press the button and the box lights up and makes a noise. The noise and light stop when they release the button.

He draws the circuit diagram shown below.

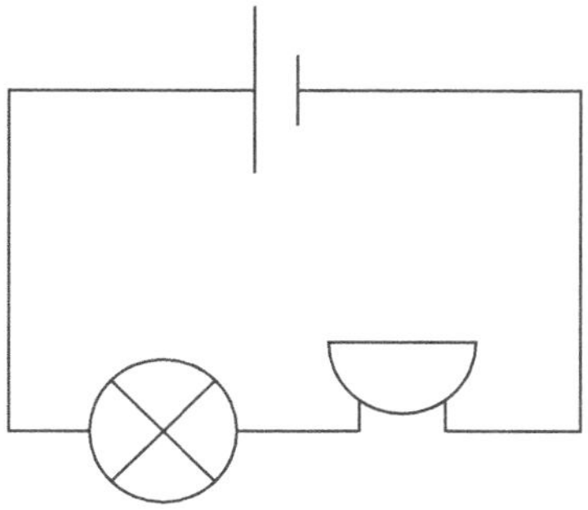

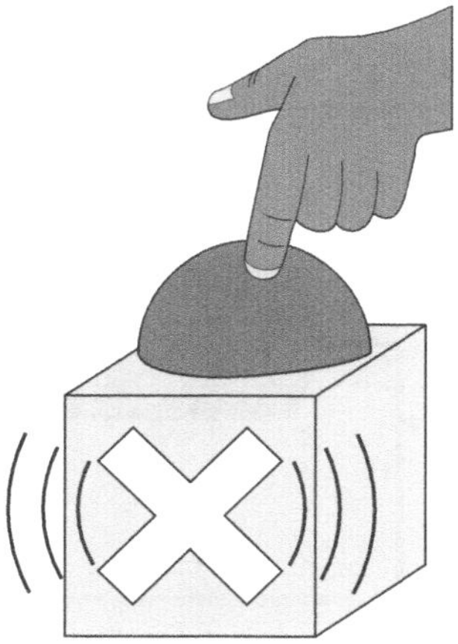

a) What component is missing from the circuit?

....

1 mark

b) Why do the bulb and buzzer only work when the button is pressed?

....

....

....

2 marks

c) Omar says the noise needs to be louder to be heard in the quiz. What change could he make to the circuit?

....

1 mark

Score: / 16

A-maze-ing Circuit

Draw wires through the maze to connect the components and make a circuit like the one shown in the diagram.

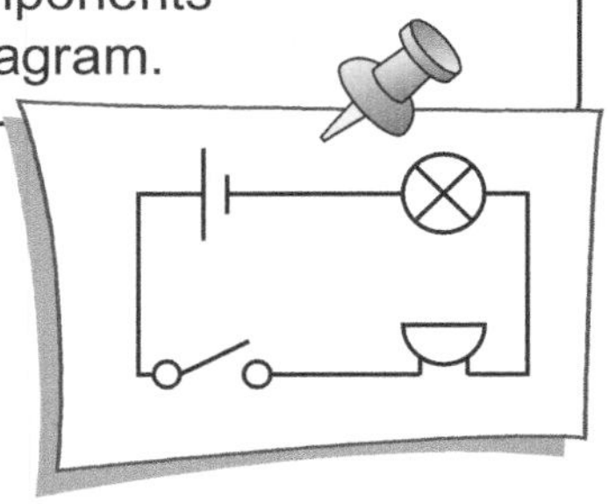

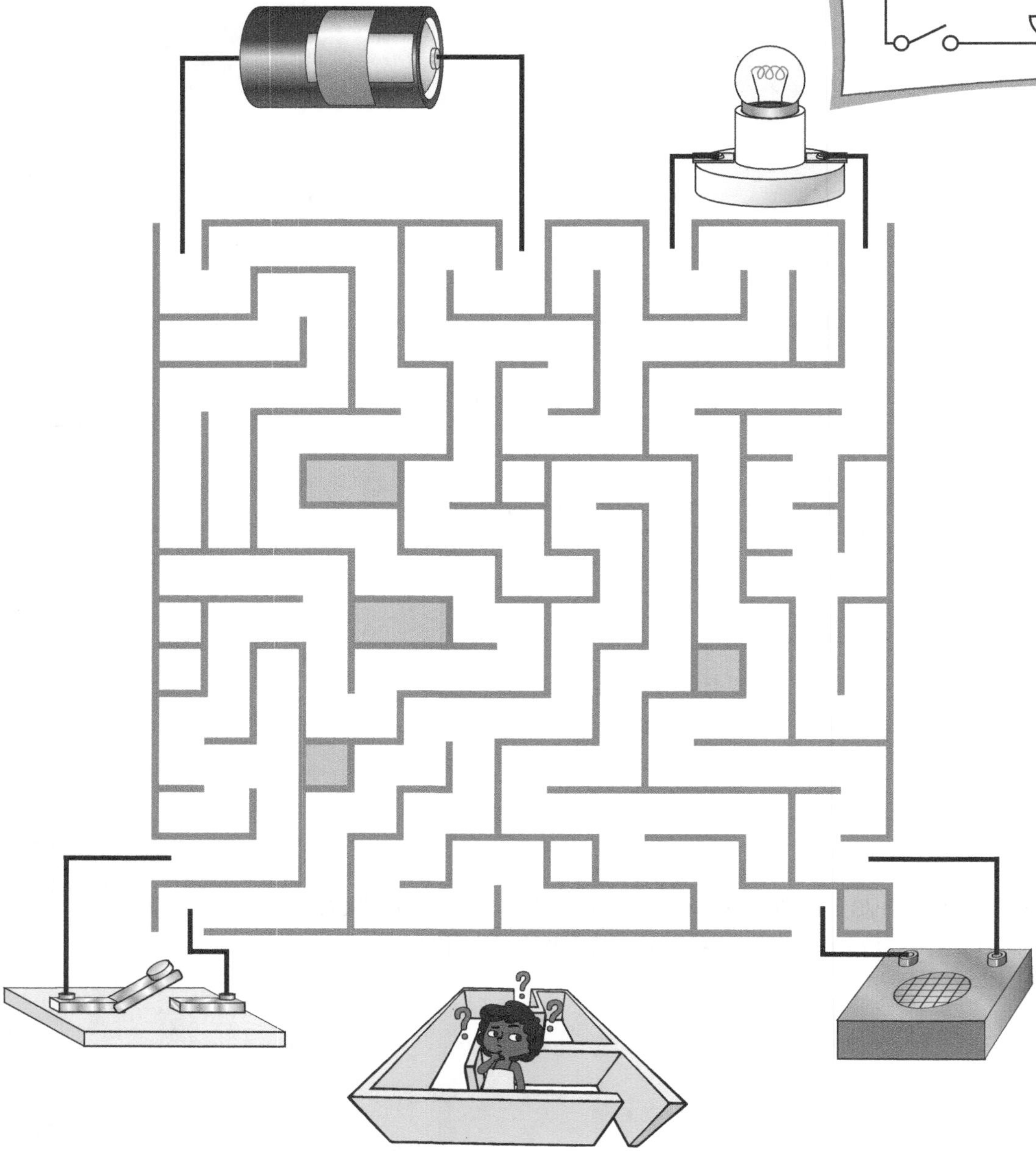

Test 1 – Mixed Test

10

Warm up

1. Look at the sheep below and tick the animal that could be its offspring.

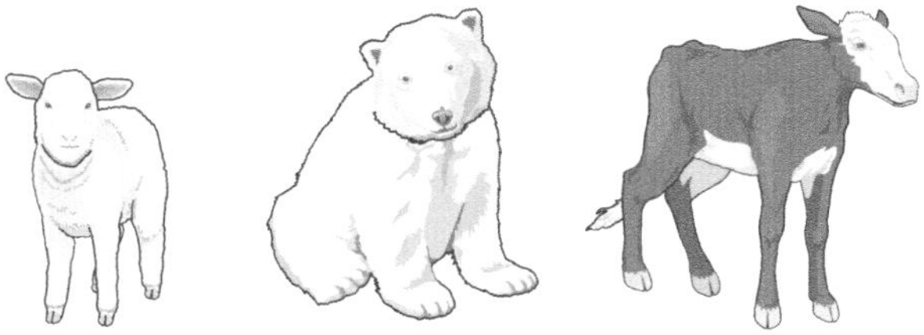

☐ ☐ ☐

1 mark

2. Complete these sentences by putting a circle around the correct word(s) in each pair of brackets.

Many drugs (**contain vitamins** / **are addictive**).

Misusing drugs can cause brain (**damage** / **growth**).

2 marks

3. Three circuit diagrams are drawn below.
Put a cross through the circuit in which the bulb won't light.
Circle the circuit in which the bulb will be the brightest.

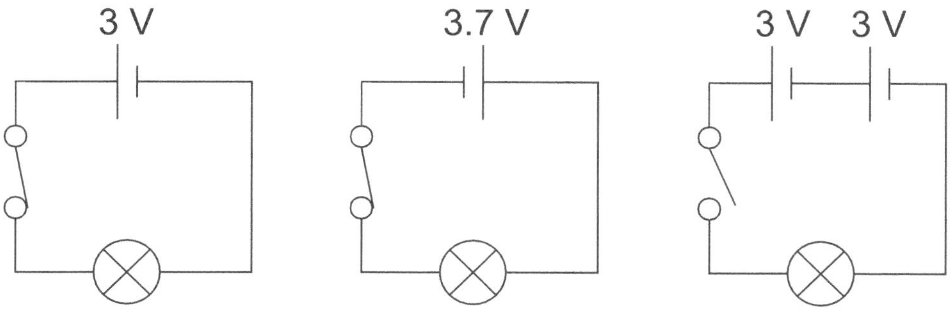

2 marks

4. Read the information about each organism below.
Draw a line to match each organism to the correct group.

jellyfish
Has no bones at all.

eel
Lays eggs in water.

sea lion
Has a steady body temperature.

fish (vertebrate)

mammal (vertebrate)

invertebrate

2 marks

5. Unscramble the three main parts of the circulatory system.

THERA ....

DOLOB ....

OLOBD SLEVESS ....

3 marks

6. Eve sees the reflection of a firework in a puddle.

Put the sentences below in order
to explain how Eve can see the firework.
The first one has been done for you.

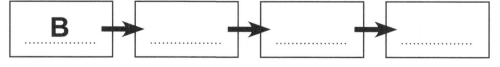

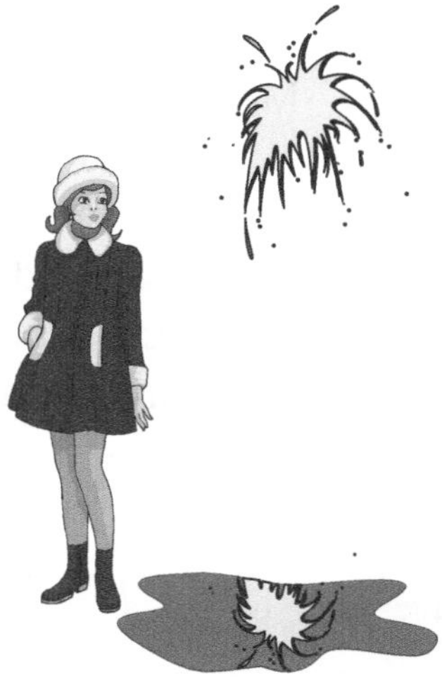

A. The light hits the puddle.

B. The firework gives out light.

C. The light enters her eye.

D. The light is reflected.

B	→	→	→ ....

2 marks

7. Penguins live in the cold, near the South Pole. Their main diet consists of seafood, which they catch when swimming in sea water.

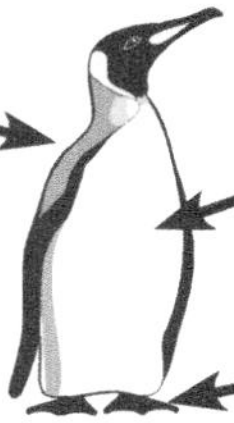

a) Choose a labelled feature of the penguin and describe how it helps penguins survive.

....

....

1 mark

Some scientists think that penguins could have once used their wings to fly. They think their wings have evolved to become better shaped for swimming instead of flying, causing them to lose their ability to fly.

b) What is meant by 'evolution'?

....

1 mark

c) Tick the sentence that correctly describes how this evolution might have happened.

- ☐ Penguins with wings better shaped for swimming were more likely to survive and produce offspring.
- ☐ Penguins with wings better shaped for flying were more likely to survive and produce offspring.
- ☐ Penguins with wings better shaped for swimming were less likely to catch fish.
- ☐ Penguins with wings better shaped for flying were more likely to catch fish.

1 mark

Score: / 15

Test 2 — Graphs, Charts and Tables

Warm up

1. Circle the piece of equipment that can be used to time how long something takes.

thermometer **stopwatch** **1 metre ruler** **protractor**

1 mark

2. Fill in the gaps in these sentences using some of the words below.

every	**success**	**one**
prediction	**fair test**	**the biggest**

To make an experiment a .... you must change

.... variable and keep everything else the same.

2 marks

3. A student investigates how the weight of a water bottle changes with the amount of water in it.
The student's results are shown in the table.
Plot the results on the graph and draw a line connecting the points.
The first point has been plotted for you.

Water in bottle (ml)	Weight of bottle (g)
40	50
35	45
20	30
10	20

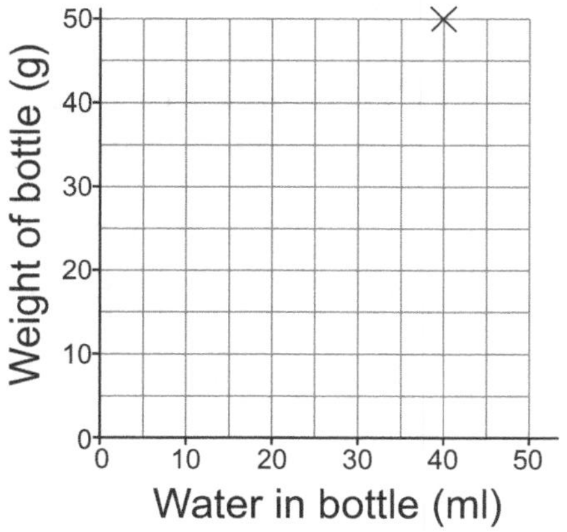

3 marks

4. Alaya sits in her garden and counts the number of invertebrates she sees in 5 minutes. She marks her results in the tally chart shown.

butterflies	~~||||~~
worms	~~||||~~ |||
wasps	||

a) Write up Alaya's results in this table.

Invertebrate	Worms	Butterflies	Wasps
Number seen			

1 mark

b) Plot the results on the bar chart below.

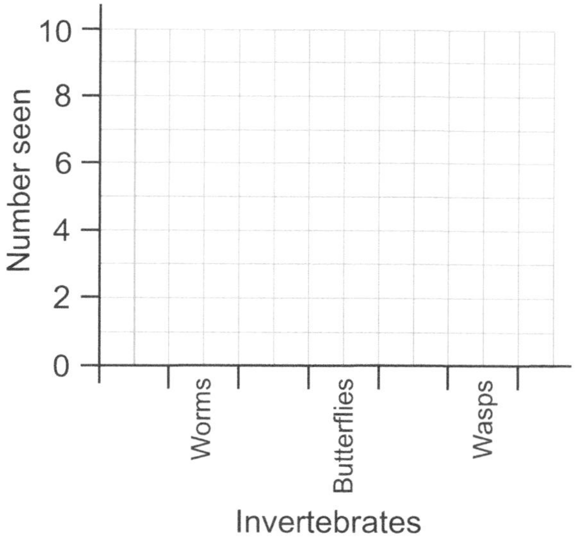

2 marks

c) Circle the correct conclusion to Alaya's investigation.

- She saw more worms in the garden than wasps at the time that she was looking.
- The wasps are scared of the worms which is why there are fewer wasps.
- There are always more worms in the garden than wasps.
- Worms like the garden more than wasps do.

1 mark

5. A student wants to see how the temperature of a cup of coffee, when placed outside, changes over time. He makes a cup of coffee, and then measures its temperature every minute for ten minutes.

His results are shown on the graph.

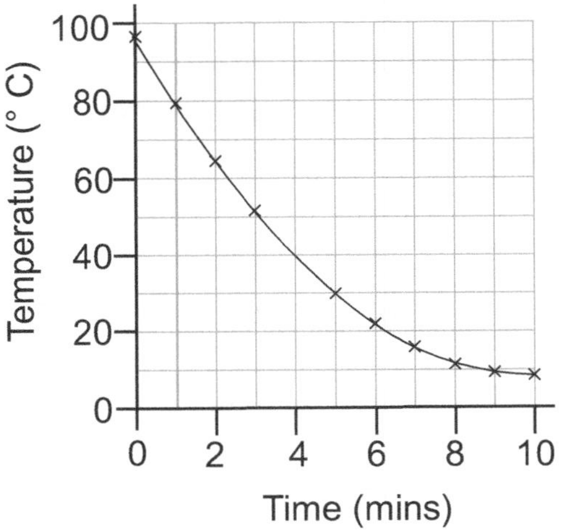

a) Describe what the graph tells you.

....

....

1 mark

The student forgot to take the coffee's temperature at 4 minutes.

b) Predict what the temperature would have been using the graph. Show your working on the graph.

....

2 marks

c) The student repeats the investigation to make sure his results are reliable. Tick the box which says what he would see in the repeated investigation if his results are reliable.

The results are very different to his original investigation. ☐

The results are very similar to his original investigation. ☐

The results are the opposite to his original investigation. ☐

1 mark

Score: / 14

What's the Word?

Fill in the missing letters to complete the definitions. Then unscramble the letters from the grey boxes to reveal a final word. Define that word on the dotted lines.

	H			O	

= a dark area made when light is blocked by an opaque object

	U		R				T	

= substances that plants and animals need to live and grow

		S	S		

= the shape of a dead animal or plant, found in a rock

			D	I					N

= what you think will happen in an experiment

				O			N	

= something that does a job in a circuit, e.g. a bulb

				R	

= blood vessel that carries nutrients and oxygen from the heart to the rest of the body

					A				

= a feature of a living thing, which helps it survive in its habitat

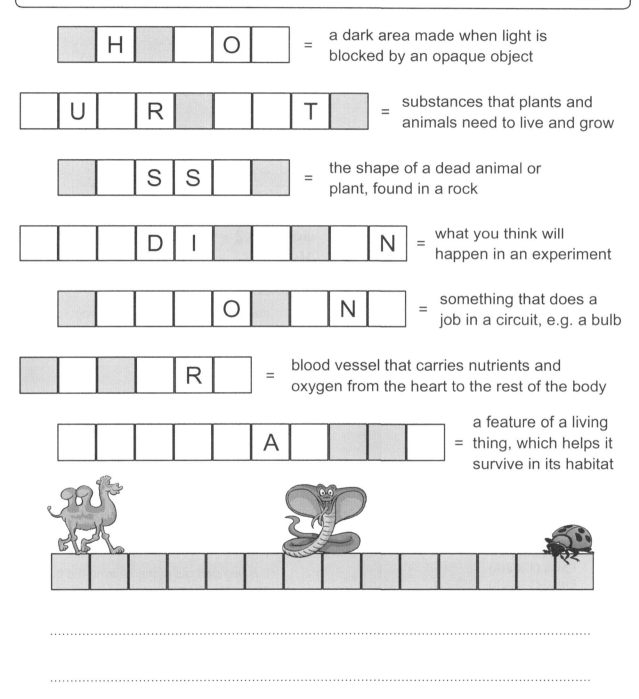

....

....

Answers

Section 1 – Living Things and Their Habitats

Getting Started – page 2

1. Animals can be divided into two groups, called vertebrates and **invertebrates**. Animals in the same group share similar **features**. Vertebrates are all animals with a **backbone**.

2. A: Mallard
   B: Mustang
   C: Seahorse
   D: Red Admiral

Test 1 – Classifying Organisms – pages 3-5

1.

Animals	Plants	Micro-organisms
octopus fox	moss oak tree	bacteria

(1 mark for each correct column)

2. a) Putting living things into different groups **(1 mark)**.
   b) It can be used to identify living things **(1 mark)**.

3. mammal **(1 mark)**
   fish **(1 mark)**

4. mammals **(1 mark)**

5. a) E.g. all plants can make their own food **(1 mark)**.
   b) E.g. some plants have flowers, whereas other plants don't **(1 mark)**.

6. True **(1 mark)**
   False **(1 mark)**
   False **(1 mark)**

7. a) Number of legs: 6
   Number of body parts: 3
   (1 mark for both correct)
   b) This organism is **an invertebrate** **(1 mark)** and it belongs in the **insect** **(1 mark)** group.

Classification Wordsearch – page 6

M	N	P	O	R	E	Q	S	W	T	Y	G	F	A	S
S	E	T	A	R	B	E	T	R	E	V	N	I	D	J
M	A	S	B	E	R	S	N	I	O	E	I	S	G	L
S	C	M	D	N	M	E	A	T	F	R	R	H	E	R
I	P	H	E	R	B	R	L	O	H	T	E	B	O	U
N	E	F	O	S	I	S	P	M	E	E	W	A	C	X
A	D	W	H	N	U	B	A	C	K	B	O	N	E	S
G	T	L	N	A	C	L	Y	K	D	R	L	I	T	E
R	M	R	F	I	L	S	U	T	P	A	F	M	R	A
O	L	Y	D	B	I	N	S	E	C	T	S	A	V	Y
O	K	V	E	I	E	A	N	P	O	E	R	L	S	A
R	F	A	R	H	Y	E	A	J	I	S	T	S	L	R
C	L	R	E	P	T	I	L	E	S	D	L	T	I	L
I	U	O	I	M	E	M	P	N	G	O	E	F	A	E
M	A	M	M	A	L	S	D	E	R	F	X	R	N	A
E	W	P	A	L	F	X	E	T	H	P	O	I	S	Z

Section 2 – Animals Including Humans

Getting Started– page 7

1. dancing, playing football, walking

2. a) proteins
   b) beans

3. rib cage

Test 1 – The Circulatory System – pages 8-10

1.

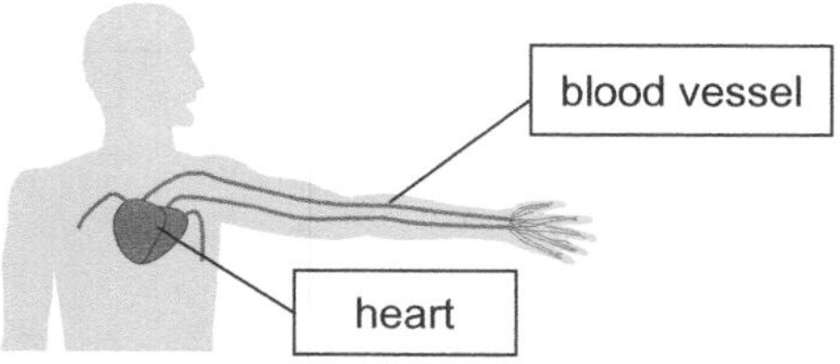

(1 mark for each correct label)

2. It is pumped out of the heart to the body and lungs **(1 mark)**.

Answers

3. This blood vessel carries blood away from the heart to the rest of the body — **Artery (1 mark)**
This blood vessel allows substances to move in and out of blood — **Capillary (1 mark)**
This blood vessel carries blood from the rest of body back to the heart — **Vein (1 mark)**

4.

Blood Vessel	Letter
Vein from the lungs	D
Artery to the body	C
Vein from the body	A
Artery to the lungs	B

(2 marks for all letters correct, otherwise 1 mark for one correct)

5. a) carbon dioxide **(1 mark)**, water **(1 mark)**, nutrients **(1 mark)**

b) Oxygen from the lungs goes into the blood **(1 mark)** and carbon dioxide from the blood goes into the lungs (and is breathed out) **(1 mark)**.

c)
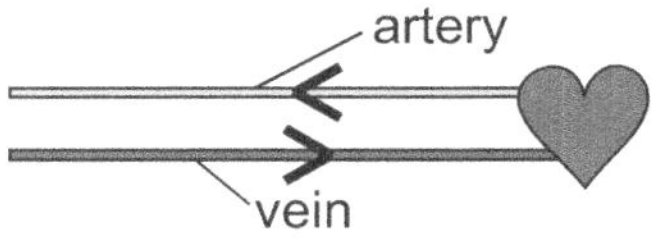

(1 mark for both arrows correct)

Test 2 – Keeping Healthy – pages 11-13

1.
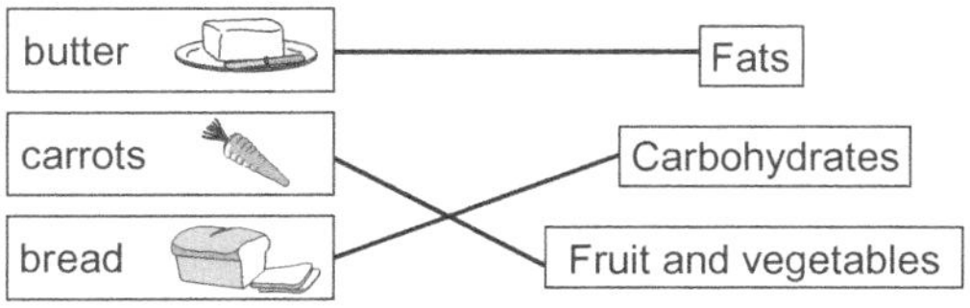

(1 mark for 1 correct answer, 2 marks for all correct)

2. kidney **(1 mark)**

3. E.g. fish / meat / milk / eggs **(1 mark for any food with protein)**

4. It helps you sleep. **(1 mark)**
It strengthens the heart. **(1 mark)**

5. a) E.g. it can cause heart attacks / blocked arteries / lung cancer / breathing problems **(1 mark)**.

b) E.g. it can damage your liver / damage your heart / damage your stomach / can cause your blood pressure to rise **(1 mark)**.

c) nicotine **(1 mark)**

6. Nutrients from food are absorbed into the **blood** from the **small** intestine. **Water** is absorbed into the body in the **large** intestine. **(1 mark for each correct word)**

7. E.g. by exercising regularly / by avoiding unnecessary health risks (such as taking drugs) / by eating a balanced diet. **(2 marks — 1 mark for each correct answer)**

8. Fibre helps food move through the gut **(1 mark)**.

Crack the Code – page 14

MBQD → VEIN
YBXEC → HEART
IEZTJ → DRUGS
BVBEOQJB → EXERCISE
DZCEQBDCJ → NUTRIENTS
OQEOZLXCHEF JFJCBS → CIRCULATORY SYSTEM
Extra word: **ARTERY**

Section 3 – Evolution and Inheritance

Getting Started – page 15

1. The environment that a living thing lives in is called its **habitat**. If this environment is **damaged**, the **organisms** living there may die if they no longer have the conditions they need, e.g. **food** and shelter.

Answers

2. The following statements should have a cross next to them, and there should be a tick next to the others:
Dead animals and plants mix with mud and sand at the surface of lakes and seas.
The hard bits of the animals and plants rot away quickly.

Test 1 – Inheritance and Adaptations – pages 16-18

1. False **(1 mark)**
True **(1 mark)**
True **(1 mark)**

2. E.g. colourful flowers help the plant attract insects for pollination / big leaves allow the plant to get as much light as possible / lots of roots allow the plant to collect water from a large area. **(1 mark)**

3. father **(1 mark)**
father **(1 mark)**

4. a) A hot desert **(1 mark)**

b) E.g. to be able to hear predators more easily **(1 mark for any suitable reason)**.

5. 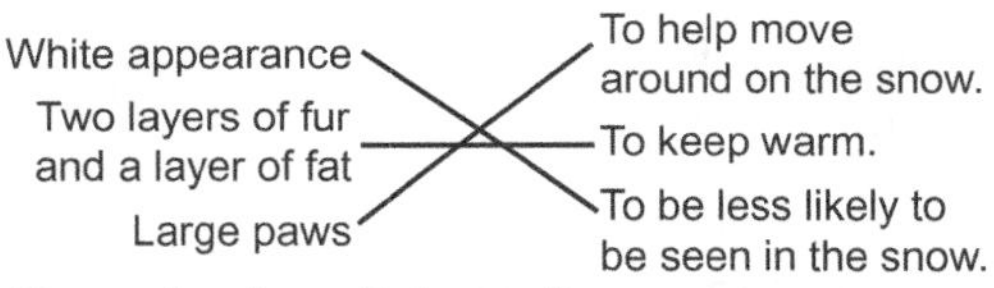

(2 marks for all three lines correct, otherwise 1 mark for one line correct)

6. a) A very tall trunk **(1 mark)**
Large leaves **(1 mark)**

b) A very smooth trunk **(1 mark)**

c) They do not live in the soil, so cannot use normal roots to get nutrients and water **(1 mark)**.

Test 2 – Evolution – pages 19-21

1. In the wild, some elephants do not develop tusks. Elephants are sometimes hunted for their tusks. Elephants without tusks are **less** likely to be hunted, so are **more** likely to survive. This means they are **more** likely to have offspring than elephants with tusks. This means that there will likely be **more** elephants without tusks than elephants with tusks over time. **(1 mark for each correct word)**

2. 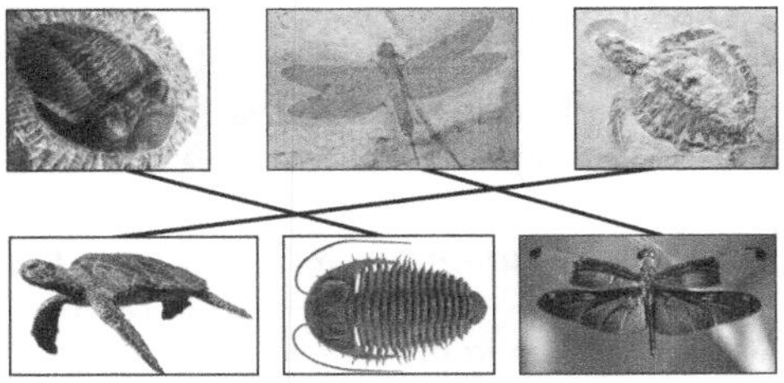

(2 marks for all three lines correct, otherwise 1 mark for one line correct)

3. a) Living things that exist today have changed over time / evolved **(1 mark)**.

b) The following statements should be circled:
Not all living things become fossils.
Not all of the fossils that exist have been found.
(1 mark for each correctly circled reason)

4. Long ago, a group of animals ate leaves from trees. When there were no more leaves on the **lower** parts of the trees, some of the animals found it hard to reach the food. The animals with slightly **longer** necks could reach the leaves higher up. These animals were **more** likely to survive and produce **offspring**, who inherited the **longer** necks.
(3 marks for all words correct, otherwise 2 marks for four words correct or 1 mark for three words correct)

5. a) An aye-aye with a long, narrow middle finger **(1 mark)**.

b) Aye-ayes with shorter tails will be worse at balancing than aye-ayes with longer tails **(1 mark)**. This means they will be less likely to survive and reproduce **(1 mark)**, so they are less likely to pass on the characteristic **(1 mark)**.

Answers

Evolutionary Crossword – page 22

The surname is DARWIN.

Section 4 – Light

Getting Started – page 23

1. 

2. If something **opaque** is in the way of a light source, it produces a shadow.
The closer the light source, **the larger** the shadow is.

3. It is reflected.

Test 1 – Light, Shadows and Reflection – pages 24-26

1. True **(1 mark)**
False **(1 mark)**

2. This option should be crossed out:
the same shape as the light source **(1 mark)**.

3. They are curved **(1 mark)**. This is wrong as light travels in straight lines **(1 mark)**.

4. 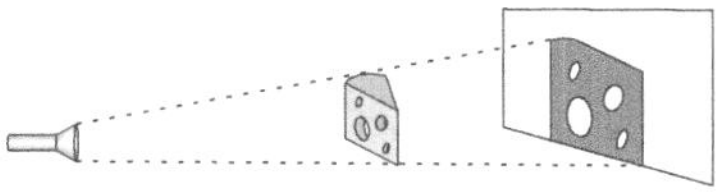

(1 mark)

5. a) E.g.

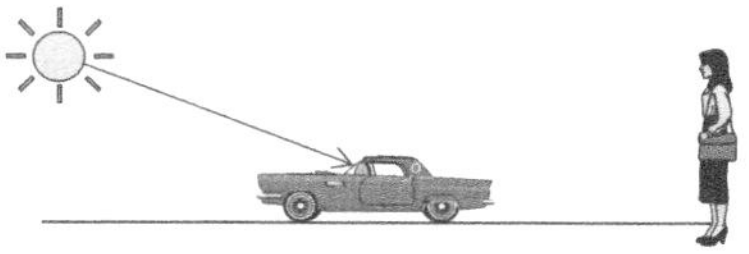

(1 mark for any arrow that is pointing away from the Sun and at the car.)

b) Light travels from the **Sun** to the car.
Light **reflects** off the car and into her eyes.
(1 mark for each correct answer)

6. a) E.g. because the candle gives out light **(1 mark)** which travels directly into his eyes **(1 mark)**.

b) traffic light **(1 mark)**

c) The light from the traffic light travels through the window and hits the mirror **(1 mark)**. It reflects off the mirror and into the boy's eyes **(1 mark)**.

Path Plotter – page 27

1. S	U		E	C	T	6. L	
	N		L			I	
H	2. S		F	E		G	
A				5. R		H	T
D	O			E			
	W	3. M		U	Q	A	
		I	R			4. P	
			R	O	R	O	

Light from the **Sun** hits a **mirror**, causing it to **reflect** onto an **opaque** object and make a **shadow** behind the object.

Section 5 – Electricity

Getting Started – page 28

1. 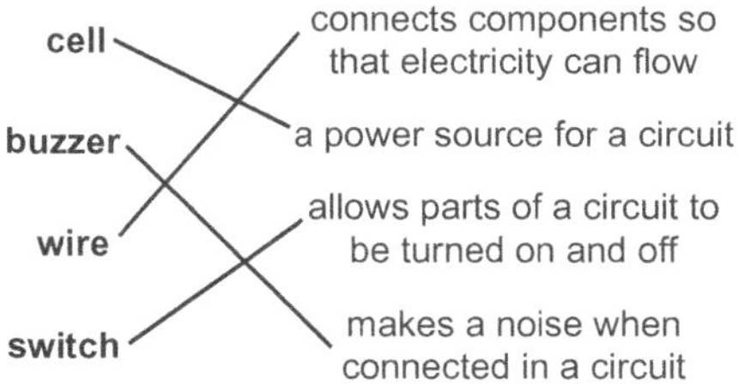

Answers

2.

3.

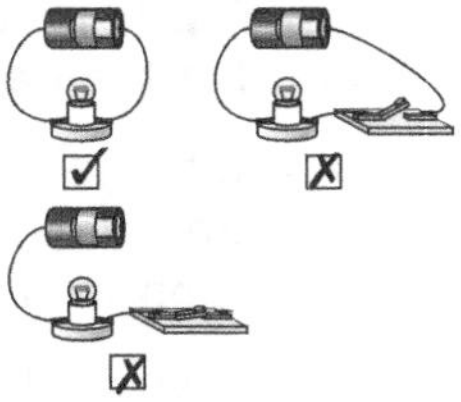

Test 1 – Circuit Components and Symbols – pages 29-31

1. —⊗— bulb

 —▽— buzzer

 —(M)— motor

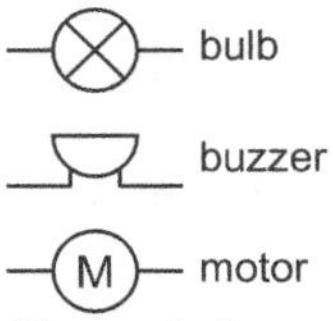

 (1 mark for each correct answer)

2. 1.5 V
 (1 mark)

3. You can increase the brightness of a bulb in a circuit by adding more **cells (1 mark)**. You could also use cells with a higher **voltage (1 mark)**.

4. E.g.

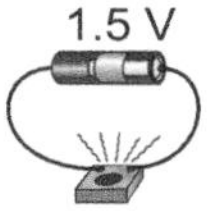

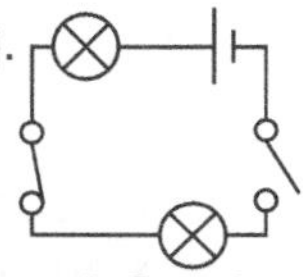

 (1 mark for drawing the bulb symbol correctly, 1 mark for drawing the cell symbol correctly, 1 mark for drawing the open and closed switch symbols correctly and 1 mark for the components joined by wires in the correct order.)

5. the switch is open **(1 mark)** a wire is missing **(1 mark)**

6. a) switch **(1 mark)**

 b) When the button is pressed, the switch closes **(1 mark)**. This completes the circuit, turning on the bulb and buzzer **(1 mark)**.

c) Add more cells / use a higher voltage cell **(1 mark)**.

A-maze-ing Circuit – page 32

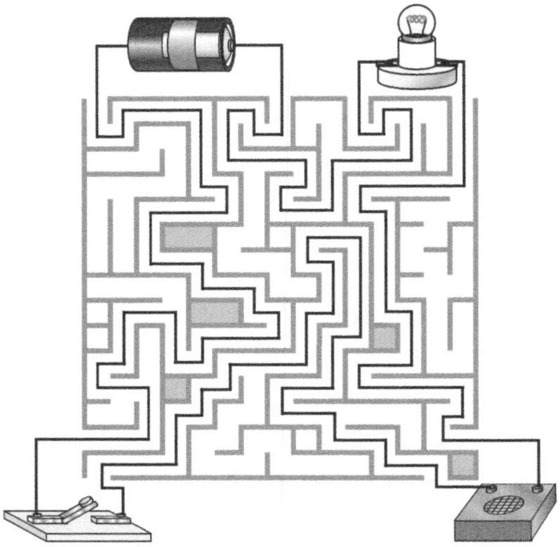

Section 6 – Mixed Practice

Test 1 – Mixed Test – pages 33-35

1. **(1 mark)**

2. Many drugs **are addictive (1 mark)**. Misusing drugs can cause brain **damage (1 mark)**.

3.
 3 V 3.7 V 3 V 3 V
 (1 mark for each)

4. **jellyfish**
 Has no bones at all. **fish (vertebrate)**
 eel
 Lays eggs in water. **mammal (vertebrate)**
 sea lion
 Has a steady **invertebrate**
 body temperature.

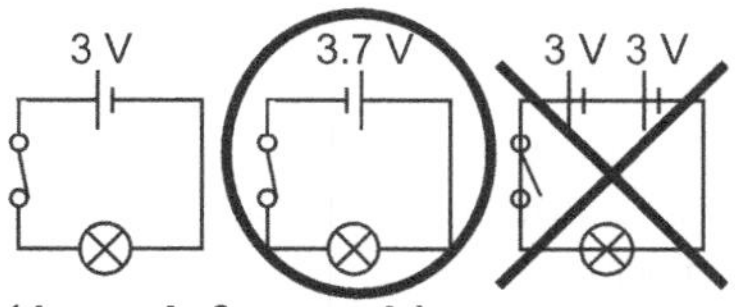

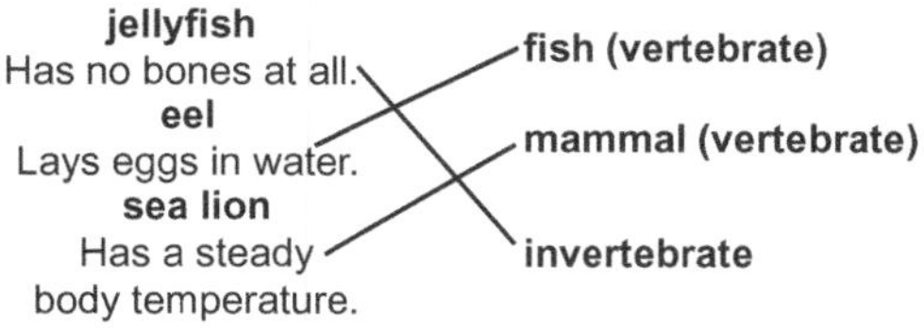

 (2 marks for all three lines correct, otherwise 1 mark for one line correct)

5. HEART
   BLOOD
   BLOOD VESSELS
   (1 mark for each)

6. B → **A** → **D** → **C**
   (2 marks for all letters in correct place otherwise 1 mark for one letter in correct place)

7. a) E.g. Webbed feet/streamlined body — helps them swim (and so catch food) **(1 mark)**. / Fat layer — keeps their body warm **(1 mark)**.

   b) E.g. living things changing over time **(1 mark)**.

   c) Penguins with wings better shaped for swimming were more likely to survive and produce offspring **(1 mark)**.

Test 2 – Graphs, Charts and Tables – pages 36-38

1. stopwatch **(1 mark)**

2. To make an experiment a **fair test** you must change **one** variable and keep everything else the same.
   (1 mark for each correct answer)

3.

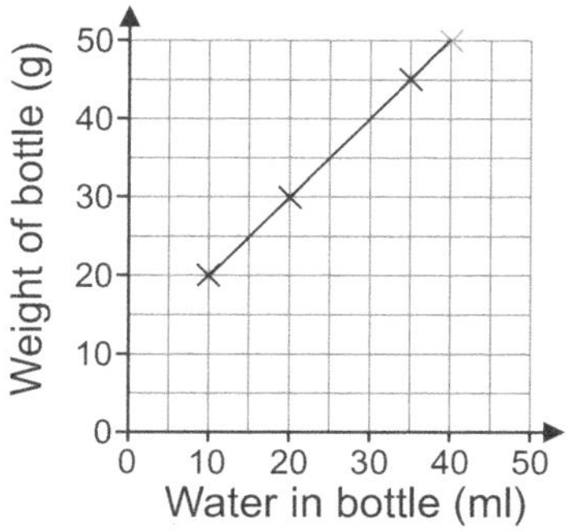

(2 marks for all three points correctly plotted or 1 mark for at least one correctly plotted. 1 mark for the line.)

4. a)

Inverte-brates	Worms	Butterflies	Wasps
Number seen	8	5	2

(1 mark for all three correct)

b)

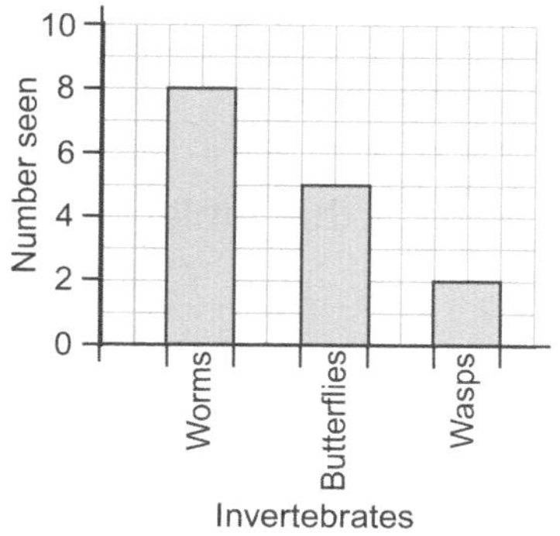

(2 marks for all correctly plotted, otherwise 1 mark for one correctly plotted)

c) She saw more worms in the garden than wasps at the time that she was looking **(1 mark)**.

5. a) The temperature of the cup decreases over time **(1 mark)**.

   b)

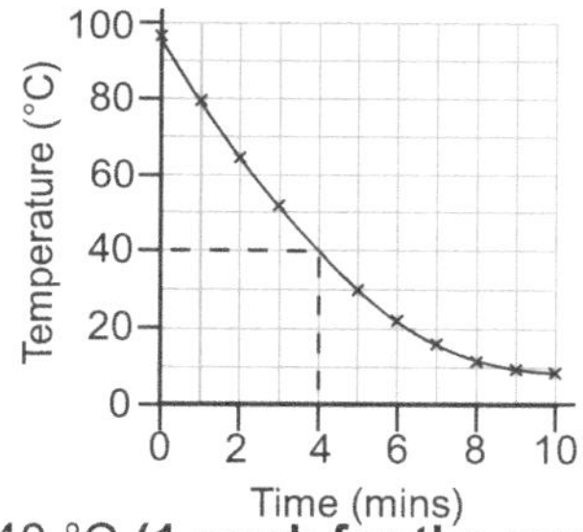

40 °C **(1 mark for the working on the graph, 1 mark for the final answer)**

   c) The results are very similar to his original investigation **(1 mark)**.

What's the Word? – page 39

SHADOW

NUTRIENTS

FOSSIL

PREDICTION

COMPONENT

ARTERY

ADAPTATION

CLASSIFICATION = putting living things into groups using their features.

Progress Chart

That's all the tests in the book done — great job!

Now fill in this table with all of your scores and see how you got on.

		Score
Living Things and Their Habitats	Test 1	
Animals Including Humans	Test 1	
	Test 2	
Evolution and Inheritance	Test 1	
	Test 2	
Light	Test 1	
Electricity	Test 1	
Mixed Practice	Test 1	
	Test 2